In the Backyard

Written and Illustrated by Trevor Pye

■ CelebrationPress

An Imprint of ScottForesman
A Division of HarperCollinsPublishers

I told my mom I saw a gigantic dinosaur
in the backyard.

Mom said, "Don't tell tales,"
and went on reading her book.

I told my dad I saw a long snake in the backyard.

Dad said, "Don't tell tales," and went on watching TV.

4

I told my brother I saw a big aardvark
in the backyard.

My brother said, "Don't tell tales,"
and went on doing his hair.

I told my best friend I saw a giant gorilla in the backyard.

My best friend said, "Don't tell tales," and went on riding his bike.

I told my neighbor I saw a huge elephant in the backyard.

My neighbor said, "Don't tell tales," and went on building her tree house.

I told my grandpa I saw an enormous lizard in the backyard.

My grandpa said, "Don't tell tales," and went on painting the pond.

13

I told my grandma I saw a large blue whale in the backyard.

My grandma said, "Oh good! Let's go and see him."

So off we went to the backyard.

15

My grandma sat down with me, and I showed her the large blue whale and all the other animals in my favorite book.